BIBLE STORIES

FOR BOYS & GIRLS

BIBLE STORIES

FOR BOYS & GIRLS

by
THEODORE W. ENGSTROM
Vice President, World Vision
Illustrations by Robert Doares

**ZONDERVAN
PUBLISHING HOUSE** OF THE ZONDERVAN CORPORATION
GRAND RAPIDS, MICHIGAN 49506

BIBLE STORIES FOR BOYS AND GIRLS
© 1948, 1971 by Zondervan Publishing House
Grand Rapids, Michigan

Library of Congress Catalog Card Number 77-146578

Second printing 1972
Third printing 1973
Fourth printing 1974

Printed in the United States of America

Contents

Introduction

Boys AND GIRLS love and need Bible stories. That is why Dr. Engstrom has retold the beloved narratives in simple but beautiful words which children will remember.

The author has not indulged his imagination: rather, he has been carefully faithful to the scriptural record. He skillfully and prayerfully relates the stories from the Word to the lives of boys and girls today.

THE PUBLISHERS

THE OLD TESTAMENT

1

A BEAUTIFUL GARDEN

(Genesis 2:8 - 3:24)

GOD made a beautiful garden. In it He placed all kinds of leafy trees and bushes. He made lovely flowers to grow in this wonderful garden.

Here God put Adam and Eve to live and enjoy all of these beautiful things. This garden was a very special place where God could meet Adam and Eve every day. He was their friend.

Birds sang their merry songs in the garden. Animals played there. It was a wonderful home. It was never too cold and never too hot.

Every fruit that is good to eat was in the garden. There were oranges and peaches and pears — and, oh, so many good fruits.

A clear, sparkling river ran through the garden.

God told Adam and Eve that He wanted them to enjoy this place. He placed all of the trees and the plants in their care. He told them to take care of all the animals and the birds.

Adam and Eve were happy as they walked about under the trees. Every day they listened to the cheerful singing of the birds. They petted all the animals they met.

God did not leave them alone. In the evening He walked in the garden. Adam and Eve often listened to His voice and talked with Him.

God gave these two people a warning. He said, "You may eat of the fruit of every tree in the garden, except of the tree of the knowledge of good and evil. If you eat of it, you will die."

For many days Adam and Eve obeyed God's command. They lived happily together in this garden.

Among all the animals there was one who was more sly than all the others. It was the serpent. Satan came to Eve in the form of this beautiful serpent. He slyly tempted her to eat the fruit from the tree whose fruit God had told them not to eat.

Satan hated God. He wanted to spoil the beautiful garden which God had made.

"Did not God say that you might eat of all the fruits of the garden?" asked the serpent.

"Yes," replied Eve. "We may eat the fruits, but we must not eat the fruit of the tree in the middle of the garden or we will surely die."

"You will not surely die," said the serpent. "But if you were to eat of the tree you would know good from evil as if you were God."

Eve wondered what kind of fruit could make her so wise. She thought how nice it would be to be as wise as God Himself. So she picked some of the fruit that looked so good. She tasted it, and then ate it.

Eve called Adam and gave him some fruit to eat.

By eating this fruit which God told them not to eat, Adam and Eve became very sinful. This was the first sin.

Satan was glad. He had made them sin.

Suddenly Adam and Eve heard the voice of God as He was walking in the garden.

He called to Adam, "Where are you?"

Adam and Eve had disobeyed God. Now they were afraid and ashamed. They knew that they had done wrong. They hid behind some trees where they thought God would not see them.

God called to Adam again and said, "Adam, where are you?"

Adam answered, "I heard Your voice, O Lord. I was ashamed and hid."

God asked, "Have you eaten of the fruit of the forbidden tree?"

Adam answered and laid the blame on Eve. "Eve gave it to me and I ate it," he said.

Eve told God that the serpent had told her to taste the fruit. So she had eaten it.

God turned to the serpent and said, "Because you have done this thing you will be cursed above all other animals. You will crawl flat on the ground all the days of your life. Men will always be your enemies. And one of them will crush your head." When God said that, He was thinking of the time when Jesus would come to this earth to crush Satan.

To Eve, God said, "I will increase your sorrow all your life as a punishment. And your husband shall rule over you."

Then to Adam, God said, "Because you listened to Eve and ate the fruit you shall work all your days for bread to eat. Weeds and thorns will make your work harder."

All of these troubles came because of sin.

God then sent Adam and Eve out of the beautiful Garden of Eden. He made them live in the world outside.

They could not go back into Eden because God put an angel at the gate with a bright, fiery sword to keep them out. No one could go into the garden.

Don't you think Adam and Eve were sorry they had disobeyed God?

The animals had been friends of Adam and Eve. Now

they were wild. The big animals growled at them. The little animals ran away from them. Because Adam and Eve sinned, God's beautiful world was spoiled.

But while God turned them out of the wonderful garden, at the same time He gave them a promise. He said that He would send a Savior to set men free from sin and death. We will learn later that this Person is the Lord Jesus. He was to come to be our Savior. He would bring us back to God.

2

AN ARK IN A FLOOD

(Genesis 6-9)

AFTER many years, more and more people lived on the earth. They forgot God. They became very wicked.

This deeply grieved God. He became angry with these wicked and sinful people. He decided to punish them by sending a great flood of water to destroy the whole world. He would destroy the people, the animals, the birds, all the flowers and every living thing.

Only one man, Noah, kept his faith in God. Noah was a good man who walked with God. God was pleased that Noah loved and served Him.

God told Noah of His plan. He asked Noah to build a large boat. This was called an Ark.

God told Noah to get ready to take his wife, his sons and sons' wives into the Ark. He also was to take two of every kind of animal with him. God promised to save these from the Flood.

Noah did as God told him to do.

Noah had three sons. Their names were Shem, Ham and Japheth. These sons helped their father build the Ark. Day after day, year after year, they worked on it.

God told Noah just how the Ark should be built. He told him how long to make it, how wide and how high it had to be. Noah made it very large and very strong. It was three stories high. There was one great door at the side and one window high at the top. God told Noah to put tar all around it, inside and out, so no water could get into it.

The neighbors stood around to watch Noah and his sons build this great boat. They all laughed at him. Noah warned them that they should repent of their sins. If they did not, God would destroy them.

The people did not listen. They did not think the Flood would ever come.

It took Noah and his sons a hundred and twenty long years to build this great Ark. Finally, when Noah was six hundred years old, the boat was finished. It stood on the dry land where all the people could see it.

Then one day God spoke to Noah again. "In seven days the rain will begin to fall," He said. "Get everything ready now."

Noah did as God said. He took his wife, his sons and his sons' wives into the Ark. With them he took two of each kind of animal. He took seven of some kinds, too.

There they came, two by two — bears, tigers, monkeys, every kind of bird, dogs, cats and all the other animals.

Can't you see the elephants plodding along, with the rabbits and the squirrels jumping ahead and the birds flying above?

Noah took food for his family and the animals and the birds into the Ark. When all of them were safely inside, God closed the door.

Soon big, dark clouds came. It started to rain a little. Then the hard rain began to fall. How glad Noah and his family were to be safely inside the warm, dry Ark!

The waters rose higher and higher. It even bubbled up out of the ground. All the people ran to the mountains for safety. They were frightened and troubled.

The great storm continued for forty long days and nights. The water covered even the highest hills.

Every person and every living thing was drowned except those who were safely in the Ark. They were not afraid, for they knew that God would take care of them.

The Flood waters covered the earth for five long months. The large Ark floated on top of this great sea.

At last the water began to go down. It went down a bit more every day. Each day the Ark came closer and closer to a resting place.

One day Noah sent out a raven from the window at the top of the Ark. The bird kept flying back and forth.

A few days later Noah sent out a dove to see whether the waters had gone down. It returned and flew around the Ark without finding a place to light. Noah put out his hand and brought the little dove back into the Ark.

Seven days later Noah sent the dove out again. It came back in the evening with an olive leaf in its beak. Noah now knew that the waters were going down and that the trees were beginning to show above it.

Another week passed. Noah sent the bird out again. This time the dove did not come back at all. Noah now knew that it had found a place to rest. He knew that the earth would soon be dry again.

God then sent a wind to dry up all the water.

Finally the Ark came to rest on the top of a great mountain. Before long, God told Noah to leave the Ark. The whole family and all of the animals came out. Think of how happy they must have been to be out of the boat and on dry land once more! The animals ran out to play on the green earth. The birds flew gaily in the blue sky.

The first thing Noah did when he came out of the Ark was to build an altar. He wanted to offer a sacrifice to thank God for His goodness.

God was pleased with Noah's sacrifice.

While Noah and his family were praying at the altar, God placed a lovely rainbow in the sky. This was His promise that never again would He send such a flood upon the earth. God promised that as long as the earth should remain there would be summer and winter, springtime and autumn, and day and night.

3

JACOB'S DREAM

(Genesis 28)

MANY years later a boy named Jacob left the home of his father and mother, Isaac and Rebekah, to go to a far land where his uncle lived. It was a long journey. Jacob was alone.

It grew dark. Jacob was tired. He was in a strange country, and he was very lonesome. After a while he wrapped himself in his coat so that he would not become cold. He lay down on the ground to sleep. He used a hard stone for his pillow.

Think how lonesome it was for Jacob out in the cold, dark desert by himself. He could hear the wild animals cry and call out in the dark.

At last Jacob fell asleep. He began to dream. In his dream he saw a tall ladder. It stood on the earth and the top reached into heaven. Jacob saw bright, shining angels of the Lord going up and down the ladder.

At the very top stood One who was much brighter than the angels. It was God Himself.

God spoke to Jacob from the top of the ladder. He said, "I am the Lord God your Father. The land on which you lie I will give to you and your sons. In your sons shall all the families of the earth be blessed. I will bring you again to this land. And I will go with you wherever you go."

These wonderful words promised to Jacob all that he had wanted.

When Jacob awoke he remembered his dream. He knew that God had talked to him. He was not alone for God had promised to be with him.

"Surely God is in this place," he said, "and I knew it not."

Then Jacob promised God to give back to Him a part of all that God should give him if God would go with him and bless him as He had promised. Jacob took the stone which was his pillow. He made an altar of it. He poured oil on top of the altar. "This marks a place to pray," he said.

Jacob knew he would kneel here to pray again on the way home to his father's house when he would return to Canaan.

Jacob named this place "Bethel," which means "The house of God."

4

BABY MOSES IN THE BULRUSHES

(Exodus 1-2)

Jacob's name was later changed to "Israel." His children and grand-children moved to Egypt and stayed there a long time. They were there for four hundred years. God richly blessed them. The Egyptians feared the Israelites because they became strong and great.

The Egyptians set harsh taskmasters over the Israelites. They made them slaves. The Egyptians did everything they could to oppress these people.

The Israelites became so many that Pharaoh made a cruel and wicked law. He said that all of the baby boys born in families of the Israelites must be thrown into the river as soon as they were born. He said, "There are too many of these people."

This caused great sorrow among the mothers of these babies.

One mother and father had a little baby boy whom they loved dearly. They did not throw him into the river. For three months this mother carefully hid her son in her home.

When she saw that she could hide her baby no longer, this mother made an ark-like basket of bulrushes. She covered this with sticky black pitch so that no water could get in. She made a soft bed in the basket. Then she laid her little baby son in the ark.

Early in the morning the mother went quietly down to the river. Carefully she placed the basket in the weeds along the edge of the river. The cradle rocked on the little waves in the water.

The mother prayed that God would keep her baby safe. She told the baby's twelve-year-old sister, Miriam, to hide nearby and watch.

That morning Pharaoh's daughter came down to bathe in the river. She saw the strange basket hidden in the weeds along the water.

"Get that strange basket," she told one of her maids. "Bring it to me."

The maid brought the ark to the princess.

The princess and her maid lifted the cover and looked at the beautiful little baby in the ark. He began to cry.

The princess wondered what to do with him.

Miriam, hiding nearby, heard the princess say, "This is one of the babies of the children of Israel."

The princess was very kind and she felt sorry for the little boy. She decided to take care of him. But she did not know how she could do so.

Miriam then came to her and asked, "Shall I call an Israelite mother to take care of the baby for you?"

The princess was pleased. She told Miriam to do this.

Miriam brought the baby's mother. Pharaoh's daughter did not know that it was the mother of the baby.

"Take this child away and care for him," the princess said. "I will pay you. When he is old enough, bring him to me."

How glad Miriam and her mother were to take the little boy back home! They could now teach him about God.

When the boy became older the mother had to bring him to the palace. The princess adopted him as her own son. She said, "I will call him Moses, which means 'Drawn Out,' because I drew him out of the water."

So Moses became a prince in the palace of the Egyptian king. He lived there for forty years. He went to the great schools of the Egyptians. Moses learned everything the wise men of Egypt knew.

But he did not forget God.

5
THE WALLS OF JERICHO FALL
(Joshua 6)

MANY years later Moses led the Israelites out of Egypt. After forty long years of wandering in the wilderness, the children of Israel finally were led into Canaan. This was the land God had promised to them. God had been very good to them. He promised that He would help them fight against the wicked people in this land.

Moses did not go into Canaan. On the top of Mount Nebo, in the wilderness, God took Moses to be with Himself. God buried him there on the mountain.

Just before Moses left the children of Israel, he told them that God had chosen Joshua to become their leader.

Joshua was a brave captain. He asked God to help him. The people all obeyed Joshua.

The Israelites came to the city of Jericho. Jericho was just across the Jordan River in Canaan. There the children of Israel set up their tents. The people waited outside the high walls which were closed tightly against them. There they waited for God to tell them what to do.

One day Joshua saw a man who looked like a soldier. He had a great sword in his hand. Joshua asked him who he was. The man answered, "I come as Captain of the Army of the Lord."

Joshua knew that He was the Lord from heaven.

God told Joshua that He would give a great victory to the Israelites if they would carefully obey His word. He told Joshua just how he was to fight against Jericho.

The people of Jericho were expecting the people of Israel to fight them. They were afraid to go outside the city walls.

Joshua told all of the men to march around the city walls. He called seven priests. Joshua told the priests to take rams' horns and blow them like trumpets. They had to walk before the ark which was carried by four other priests. Then Joshua told some of the soldiers to go before the priests. He told the rest to walk behind the priests. He told them to be very quiet until he ordered them to shout.

This was certainly a strange way to fight.

The next day Joshua made the people and the priests walk all the way around the city in the same way. He then sent them back to their tents again. The children of Israel did this for six days without doing any fighting.

Each day as they went around the wall the priests blew their horns.

The people of Jericho saw the people and heard the trumpets. They wondered just what was going to happen next.

On the seventh day Joshua told the Israelites to get up very early, as soon as it was light. He told them to walk around the walls as before. But when they completed the circle around the walls, Joshua did not tell them to go back to their tents. The Israelites walked around and around the city seven times.

When they finished the seven trips around, Joshua said to the people, "When the priests blow their horns we will all shout. God will make the walls of Jericho fall."

Then Joshua gave the signal. The priests blew the horns, the men gave a great shout, and the great stone walls came tumbling down! What a great crash it was! The Israelites knew that God had caused the walls to fall, because they had not even touched them.

The men of Israel ran into the city. They killed the wicked people. They set fire to the city. They burned everything. God had commanded them not to take anything.

Jericho was a very wicked city. Because of this, God destroyed it.

6

SAMSON, THE STRONG MAN

(Judges 14-16)

God made Samson, one of the men of Israel, the strongest man in the world. No one was as strong as Samson.

One day Samson seized a fierce, roaring lion which came after him. Samson was not afraid. He caught the lion by its mouth and tore it to pieces.

Another time, to punish the Philistines who were enemies of Israel, Samson caught three hundred foxes. He tied fire-brands to their tails and sent them two by two through the grain fields of the Philistines. The fields were all set on fire.

One day Samson met a Philistine woman whom he loved. Her name was Delilah. The rulers of the Philistines learned of this. They came to Delilah and said, "Find out from Samson what makes him so strong, and tell us. We will pay you much money."

So Delilah coaxed and begged Samson to tell her what made him so strong.

Samson said to her, "If you will tie me with seven green twigs from a tree, then I shall not be strong any more."

Delilah did this while Samson slept. But when he awoke he broke the bonds easily. Samson told Delilah many other things. But he did not tell her the secret of his strength.

At last Samson gave in to this wicked woman's pleading. He told her the real secret of his strength.

"My mother made a vow to the Lord that I was not to drink wine and not to allow my hair to be cut," said Samson. "If I did this the Lord would take my strength away. Then I would be like other men." Samson knew that as long as he obeyed God, He made him strong.

Delilah knew that she had found the truth at last. She told the rulers of the Philistines, "Come and you shall have your enemy. He has told me his secret."

While the Philistines waited, Samson fell asleep with his head on Delilah's lap. While he was sound asleep she called in a man to cut off his great locks of hair.

Then suddenly Delilah cried, "Rise up, Samson! The Philistines are upon you!"

Samson awoke. He expected to find himself as strong as before. At first he did not know that his hair had been cut. His vow to the Lord had been broken. God had left him. He was now no stronger than any other man. Samson could not defend himself from the Philistines.

The Philistines took Samson. They brought him to prison. They put out his eyes, so that he might never again do them harm. They made him work as though he were an animal.

While Samson was in prison his hair grew long again. With his hair his strength returned, for he renewed his vow to the Lord.

One day the Philistines held a great feast. They praised their heathen gods and offered sacrifices to them. Then they sent for Samson to torment him. "Let us have fun with him," they said.

Samson said to a little boy leading him, "Take me to the front of the temple so that I may lean against the pillars."

As he followed the boy, Samson prayed to God. He said, "Give me strength, O God, only this once. Help me that I may get revenge upon the Philistines for my eyes."

The Philistines laughed at Samson. He had been so strong.

Now he was blind and weak. The Philistines made fun of him.

Samson then placed his arms around the temple pillars on both sides of him. He bowed his head and prayed. "O God," he said, "let me be strong again just once more."

Samson then pulled with all his strength. The pillars cracked — and broke. The roof of the temple fell upon all those who were under it. Samson himself was among those killed.

In his death Samson killed more of the Philistines than he had killed during his entire life. He showed the Philistines that God was stronger than their heathen gods.

7

DAVID AND GOLIATH

(I Samuel 16–17)

MANY years later another brave man came along. A shepherd boy by the name of David lived in the city of Bethlehem during the days when Samuel was a prophet.

As David was the youngest of seven sons, he had to take care of his father's sheep out in the fields. Early every morning young David would leave his father's house and go out to the sheepfold. He would call the sheep and they would follow him.

One day a lion broke into David's flock of sheep. The lion caught a little lamb and started to drag it away. The poor little lamb was so frightened it cried out, "Baa, baa."

David heard the lamb cry. He ran quickly after the lion. God made David strong. He took the frightened lamb out of the lion's mouth and killed the lion.

Another day a bear came into the flock and was carrying a lamb away. David ran after the bear. Again God made him strong. He took the lamb from the bear's mouth and killed the bear. David was strong like Samson.

One day God told Samuel the prophet to go to the village of Bethlehem. The people saw him coming. "Samuel, the prophet has come," they said to each other.

Samuel told them, "We will have a feast together. We will worship God. Tell the people to get ready."

Jesse, David's father, and David's seven brothers got ready. But David could not come to the feast. He had to stay with the sheep.

At the feast Samuel said, "God has sent me to anoint one of the sons of Jesse. I will pour oil on the head of the one God chooses. Some day he will be king of Israel."

Jesse told his sons to walk past Samuel. All seven young men walked past the prophet, one by one.

But God did not choose any of them.

Then the prophet asked Jesse, "Are these all your sons?"

Jesse told him that one, the youngest boy, David, was out in the fields tending the sheep. "But he is just a boy," said Jesse.

"Send for him quickly," said Samuel.

David came in from the fields. He hurried to the feast. Samuel saw David coming and he heard the Lord say, "Arise and anoint him, for this is he."

Then Samuel took some oil and poured it on David's head. He anointed him. The Spirit of God came upon David. In this way God showed the people His choice. He chose David to be the second king of Israel.

One day David's father sent him on an errand. He sent him to the camp of the king's army where three of David's brothers were staying. "Bring this food to your brothers," the father said. "See if they are all well."

As David came to the king's army, he looked across the valley. On the opposite hill he saw another large army. This was the army of the Philistines who were trying to take his own king's country.

As David looked down the hillside he saw a strong man more than ten feet tall. He was bigger than any man David had ever seen. His heavy clothing was made of metal. He had a great sword in his hand.

Two times a day, for forty days, he had been walking up

and down the valley. He was mocking and making fun of God and King Saul and his army. "You say you have a wonderful God," the giant said, "but not one of you dares to come to fight me."

All of the soldiers of Israel were afraid of this giant because of his great size.

David stood and listened to this giant for a while. Then he said, "I would not be afraid to go."

When King Saul heard what David had said, he called for David. "How can you fight this giant?" Saul asked. "You are not big enough."

David told the king how he had, with God's help, killed a lion and a bear. "I am not afraid of this giant," he said.

David walked down the hill. He had his slingshot with him. By the side of a brook he picked up five smooth stones.

When Goliath saw the shepherd boy coming with his slingshot, the giant laughed and laughed. "Do you think I am a dog?" he asked.

David said to him, "You come to me with a sword and with a spear and with a shield. But I come to you in the name of the Lord of hosts."

David took his slingshot and put a stone in it. He whirled it around his head. Then he let it go. The stone went straight to the forehead of the giant. Goliath fell dead!

The soldiers of Israel shouted for joy. The Philistines began to run away. But the children of Israel chased them until not one was left.

With God's help the young shepherd boy had saved the king's army by using a slingshot and a little stone. God had been with him.

That night the people of Israel sang songs about David. The king took him to live in the palace.

8

THE BRAVE MEN IN
THE FIERY FURNACE

(Daniel 3)

LATER ON some more brave men came along. Nebuchad-nezzar was king of Babylon. He conquered all the nations around him and brought many captives to his great city. Among these captives were many boys and girls.

The king trained all of the young men among his captives whom he thought would be good soldiers and leaders. In this way he picked a young man named Daniel and three of his best friends. He wanted these young men to be rulers in his kingdom.

The king was very proud of his power. He began to think that he was as great as God Himself.

One day the king ordered a large golden image, ninety feet high, to be made. This image was higher than a house. He said that the people must fall down and worship it.

The king added an awful punishment for all those who did not obey his order. Those who did not fall down and worship this idol would be thrown into a large furnace of fire. Think how terrible that would be!

All the people did as Nebuchadnezzar wanted — except the three young Hebrew men, Shadrach, Meshach and Abed-nego. They did not bow down at all.

Servants of the king were watching these boys. They told

the king that the three young men did not bow down and worship the golden image.

The king was angry. He called all three boys before him and told them that he would give them just one more chance. He said that if they did not fall down before the idol, the next time they would be thrown into the fiery furnace.

The three men were not afraid of the king. "Who is that God who shall deliver you out of my hand?" asked the king. He asked this because he believed they were trusting in the God of Israel.

The three brave boys answered that they believed the God they served would be able to deliver them from the furnace. But even if He did not, they would not worship the golden image.

Nebuchadnezzar was terribly angry. He ordered the furnace to be heated seven times hotter than usual. He told his servants to tie the young men and throw them right into the raging fire.

The fire burned so hot in the furnace that the soldiers who threw the three men into it were burned to death.

The king came to see them burn. Imagine his surprise when he looked into the fire and saw the three men walking in the furnace. They were unbound and unhurt. The king then saw a fourth man walking with them. He seemed to be as the Son of God.

The king was frightened and asked, "Did we not cast three men into the midst of the fire?"

"Yes, O king," replied the servants.

This fourth person was an angel of the Lord walking with the young men in the flames.

The king came near the door of the fiery furnace. He called to the young men. Out they walked. As they came he saw that not a hair of their heads was burned, neither were their clothes burned. He could not even smell smoke upon them. They were unharmed.

The king promoted the three boys. He was changed by this miracle. He said that any person who would speak evil of the God of Israel would be destroyed.

God always takes care of those who love and serve Him.

9

DANIEL IN THE LIONS' DEN

(Daniel 6)

DANIEL was a man who loved God. Three times a day he would kneel by his window and pray to God.

Some men hated Daniel because he was a friend of the king. The king had made him the greatest man in the kingdom. These men were jealous. They tried to catch Daniel doing something wrong. They said to each other, "We must find something wrong with Daniel so that we can get rid of him."

But finally the men saw that it was useless. They could find nothing wrong in Daniel's life.

At last they thought of a plan. They went to the king. They said, "O king, you are very great. We want to make a new law to honor you. Make a law that no one can pray to any god for thirty days. The people may only ask you for the things they want. If anyone does pray to a god, he must be thrown into a den of lions."

The king thought, "That will make me like a god." So he made the law.

Daniel's enemies watched him. They looked through the window and saw him kneel to pray. He still prayed to God three times a day.

The men hurried to tell the king about this.

The king was sorry when he heard it. He wished that

he had not made the law, because he liked Daniel. He did not want to throw him in the den of lions. But the king had to do what he had said. He had made this law.

The king sent for Daniel. He said, "Your God, whom you serve, can save you."

Daniel was thrown into a den with great, roaring lions. The lions were hungry. They walked all around Daniel — but they did not touch him.

The king could not sleep all that night. He was thinking about Daniel in the den with the lions.

As soon as it was daylight the king went to the door of the lion's den.

He called, "Daniel, Daniel! Did your God save you?"

Daniel called back from the dark den. "Yes, O king. God sent an angel to shut the lions' mouths. They did not hurt me."

The men took Daniel out of the lions' den. The king was so happy. He made another law. He said, "The God of Daniel is the real God. Let everyone serve him."

THE NEW TESTAMENT

10
JESUS IS BORN
(Luke 1:5 - 2:40)

MANY more years went by. In the little town of Nazareth, lived Mary and her husband Joseph, a carpenter. A message came to Joseph and Mary from Caesar, the king. It said that all the people had to go to Bethlehem to pay their taxes.

Mary and Joseph loaded their donkey and went to the city.

It was late when they reached the town of Bethlehem. They asked at the inns for a place to spend the night. But there was no room for them in any inn.

Finally one inn-keeper told Mary and Joseph that they could spend the night in his stable. It was the only place they could find.

Round about them were lowing cattle and baa-ing sheep. It was a strange place to stay all night.

That night a Baby, the Lord Jesus, was laid in the manger.

On the hills outside of Bethlehem were shepherds who were watching their sheep. All was dark and still. The sheep were asleep on the green grass. The shepherds talked quietly together.

Then suddenly, angels, in all the brightness of heaven, came down to these shepherds and said to them, "Fear not: for, behold, I bring you good tidings of great joy, which shall be to all people. For unto you is born this day in the city of David a Savior, which is Christ the Lord."

Then the angels began to sing and praise God. They sang, "Glory to God in the highest, and on earth peace, good will toward men."

When the angels left them, the shepherds said to each other, "Let us go to Bethlehem. We must see the wonderful Baby."

They went quickly into the town. There they found the Christ Child lying in fresh, sweet hay. He was warmly wrapped in swaddling clothes. They knew that this Baby was the Savior. They knelt to worship Him.

These shepherds were the first ones to tell the story of Jesus. They went about saying, "Our Savior has come."

People have been telling this wonderful story ever since. It seems as new and beautiful today as it ever was.

11

JESUS AT A WEDDING

(John 2:1-11)

JESUS was now a full-grown man. In Cana, a little town in Galilee, lived some friends of Jesus and His mother.

One day these people invited Jesus and His mother and many other friends to attend a wedding. This was held in the home of the bridegroom.

It was a happy wedding feast. They had many good things to eat and drink. But these people did not make enough wine for everyone who came. Soon all of it was gone. They had nothing to drink.

Jesus' mother saw that the wine pitchers were empty. She went to tell Jesus about it. She knew His power and believed that He could help at a time like this. She told the servants who waited on the tables to do whatever Jesus told them to do.

Six large stone water pots were standing near by. Jesus called to some of the servants. He told them to fill the water pots with fresh, clean water.

The servants did as Jesus said. Then Jesus told them to take this water out of the pots and fill the wine pitchers again. When they did this they found that new pure wine came from the pots which they had just filled with water. The water had been turned to wine!

Jesus told the servants to take this new wine to the ruler of the feast. The ruler had to taste it first of all.

The ruler did not know that Jesus had made more wine. When he tasted it he showed that he was surprised. It was so much better than the first wine which had been served. He said that at most feasts the best wine was served first. "But," he said, "you have kept the best wine until now."

This was the first of many miracles which Jesus did.

12

JESUS CALLS HIS DISCIPLES

(Matthew 4:18-22; 9:9-13; Mark 1:16-20; John 1:43-51)

ONE morning two fishermen, Andrew and Simon, were busy working in their fishing boat along the Sea of Galilee.

As they were working, the fishermen looked up. There they saw Jesus walking along the shore. Jesus called to them and said, "Follow Me and I will make you fishers of men."

The two fishermen left their boats and followed Jesus.

Farther along the shore Jesus saw two other fishermen who were busy mending their torn nets. These men were brothers — James and John. They worked with Simon and Andrew as fishermen. Jesus called to these two also. They put their nets down at once. They asked their father and their servants to take care of the fishing business.

Another day Jesus was walking along a street in the city of Capernaum. He saw a man named Matthew taking tax money from the people. The Jews did not like these tax collectors. Jesus saw Matthew's heart and knew he would be a good disciple. He told the publican to follow Him.

Matthew obeyed and left his money table to follow Jesus. He later wrote the first of the four Gospels.

All together there were twelve men who became Jesus' trusted followers. He wanted these men so that He could prepare them for His work. This work would have to be carried on after He went to heaven.

Jesus called other disciples — Philip, Nathanael, another James, another Simon, Judas the brother of James, and Judas Iscariot, who finally betrayed Jesus.

Jesus told His disciples that He would give them power to heal the sick, even lepers. He would give them power to raise the dead. He called them "apostles," which means "those who are sent."

Jesus told His twelve helpers to take no money with them. They were not even to take extra clothing or anything to eat. Jesus knew that they would be cared for by the people they helped.

13

JESUS AT THE WELL

(John 4:1-30)

ONE day Jesus and His disciples left the country of Galilee to go to Judea. To get to Judea they had to pass through the land of Samaria.

The people who lived in this country were called Samaritans. They hated the Jews with a bitter hatred. The Jews and the Samaritans were enemies.

One morning on the journey Jesus stopped to rest beside an old well. This well had been dug by Jacob many years before. Jacob had called it Sychar.

Jesus sent His disciples into the near-by village to buy food. He stayed at the well. He was thirsty as well as hungry. But Jesus had no rope to let down a cup to draw water from the well.

A Samaritan woman came near with a heavy water jar on her head. This was the way they carried water in those days.

Jesus asked the woman for a drink.

This Samaritan woman knew from His clothes that Jesus was a Jew. She also knew that Jews did not often speak to Samaritans.

The woman wondered who this stranger could be. She knew that He was not like other Jews. They would rather be thirsty than ask a Samaritan for water.

"How is it that you, a Jew, ask a drink from me, a Samaritan?" she asked.

Jesus replied, "If you knew who it was that asked you for a drink you would ask Him to give you a drink of the living water. And He would give it to you. Whoever drinks of this water shall thirst again; but whoever drinks of the water I shall give him shall never thirst, but the water I shall give him shall be in him a well of water springing up into eternal life."

Jesus knew the heart of this sinful woman. He showed her that He knew all about her. He told her that she was living a wicked life.

The disciples returned from the city. They were surprised to find that Jesus was speaking to this woman.

The Samaritan woman left her water jar at the well and started back to the city. There she told her friends, "Come, see a man that told me everything I did." She knew that Jesus was the Savior of the world.

All the people of Samaria saw the change in this woman after she met Jesus. They came to Him and asked Him to stay there in that country for a time.

Jesus and His disciples spent two days in Samaria teaching the people about God. Many of the Samaritans believed on Him.

14

PETER WALKS ON THE WATER

(Matthew 14:22-33; Mark 6:45-51; John 6:16-21)

ONE night Jesus was all alone on the mountainside. He was kneeling on the green grass, praying to His Heavenly Father. His disciples were in a little boat out in the middle of a lake. Jesus had told them to row to the other side.

The wind began to blow fiercely. The waves were dashing high. The water was rough. The little boat was tossing about like a cork.

The disciples pulled as hard as they could at the oars, but they could not get closer to the shore. Of course they were afraid.

Jesus looked across the water and saw the boat in the storm. He began to walk out on the stormy waves.

Suddenly across the water the disciples saw a white figure appear. They were frightened. They thought that it must be a ghost.

Then the figure called to them and said, "Be of good cheer; it is I; be not afraid." The disciples knew then that it was Jesus. They recognized His wonderful voice.

Peter, one of the disciples, was so glad that for a minute he was not afraid of anything. He said, "If it is really You, Lord, tell me to come to You on the water."

"Come," said Jesus.

Peter started out of the boat. He looked at Jesus and

walked on the top of the water just as Jesus did. As long as Peter looked on Jesus' face he stayed on top. But suddenly Peter looked at the waves and the water around him. He was afraid.

Then Peter began to sink into the water. He called out fearfully, "Lord, save me."

Quickly Jesus took him by his hand and said, "Why are you afraid?" Why should Peter be afraid when Jesus was with him?

Jesus and Peter walked together on the waves. They stepped into the boat where the other disciples were. The wind stopped blowing and the sea became still and calm. The disciples could now row very easily.

They all crowded around Jesus and said, "Truly Thou art the Son of God."

Even the wind and the waves obeyed His will.

15

JESUS QUIETS A STORM

(Matthew 8:23-27; Mark 4:36-41; Luke 8:22-25)

ONE day Jesus, with His disciples, wanted to go across the Sea of Galilee. He wanted to go where it was quiet and peaceful so that He could rest. He was tired.

Jesus took His disciples into Peter's small fishing boat. He told them to row across the sea. Jesus went to the back part of the boat and lay down to rest. He was soon sound asleep.

Suddenly, as often happened on the Sea of Galilee, a fierce storm came up. The wind blew harder and harder. The small boat tossed everywhere. The waves grew higher and higher. The big waves began to roll over the boat. The disciples thought that the boat would sink and they would all drown.

Jesus slept on even though the water was splashing into the boat and the waves were tossing it around, up and down, back and forth.

The disciples became terribly afraid. They awakened Jesus and said, "Master, don't You care if we perish?"

Jesus awoke. He came to the front of the boat. He turned and calmly looked at the storm and the black skies. Then He said to His disciples, "Why are you so fearful? Why don't you have faith?"

Jesus was not afraid.

The Master then stretched out His hands over the water. He spoke to the low-hanging dark sky, the churning sea and the wind that was screaming and tearing at the boat. "Peace, be still," said Jesus.

At once all was calm and quiet. The sun peeped through the clouds. The sea became as smooth as glass. The wind became a little whisper. The Master had spoken. Jesus had made and created the wind and the water, so He was able to still the storm.

The disciples looked at each other and said, "What manner of Man is this, that even the winds and the sea obey Him?"

Truly Jesus is the master even of nature itself.

He can be the master of the storms that arise in our hearts and lives because of our sin, too, and if we trust in Him, He can and will quiet them. He will forgive us and give us peace in our hearts.

16

FIVE THOUSAND PEOPLE ARE FED

(Matthew 14:13-21; Mark 6:30-44; Luke 9:10-17;
John 6:1-13)

ANOTHER day Jesus and His twelve disciples went into a
fishing boat. They sailed down the Sea of Galilee so that
the Master could get some rest.

A great crowd of men and women, and boys and girls,
followed Jesus. When the little boat came to shore, all the
people were right there. They wanted to be where Jesus
was.

That day Jesus spent much time teaching the people and
healing their sick. Blind people were made to see. Crippled
children could walk again. The deaf could hear.

As it grew late in the day the disciples told Jesus to send
all the people home. But the great crowd did not want to
leave. Even though they were tired and hungry, they wanted
to be with Jesus.

The disciples began to wonder how all these people were
going to be fed. There was no food anywhere. Then the
disciples noticed that one young boy had his lunch with him.

Andrew, a disciple, told Jesus about this boy. He told
Jesus that the little fellow had five small barley loaves and
two small fishes in his lunch.

Jesus asked the boy to give Him the loaves and the fishes.
The lad willingly did what Jesus asked him.

Jesus said to His disciples, "Tell all the people to sit down."

The people did so. The green hill was covered with people.

Jesus then took the boy's lunch, looked up to His Father in heaven, and thanked Him for it. He divided the loaves and the fishes.

The disciples passed the food piece by piece to the people. They all ate. Everyone had enough to eat. No one was hungry.

The Lord then told the disciples to gather all that was left. They did as Jesus said. They found that there was enough left to fill twelve baskets.

Jesus had made enough food from the five loaves and the two fishes to feed five thousand men, and all the women and the children.

"Truly," all the people said, "this is the Messiah."

17

THE LITTLE CHILDREN
COME TO JESUS

(Matthew 19:13-15; Mark 10:13-16; Luke 18:15-17)

Jesus went with His twelve disciples from place to place comforting those who were in sorrow and healing the sick people. Wherever He went there were little children who came to see Him. He was always good and kind to them. He wanted them to know and love Him.

One day, while Jesus and His followers were resting along the road, they saw a great crowd of people coming toward them. Many small children were in the crowd. And babies were there, too.

Peter asked these people what they wanted.

They said that they wanted Jesus to bless the little boys and girls.

Andrew, another of the disciples, stepped up and told them that Jesus was too tired and weary to be bothered with all of those children then.

The mothers and children were very unhappy. They wanted Jesus to bless the children.

But Jesus spoke to the people and said, "Suffer the little children to come unto Me, and forbid them not, for of such is the kingdom of heaven."

Then Jesus took the smaller children lovingly in His arms and blessed them. He put His arms around the bigger ones.

All the boys and girls crowded around Him. They could not help loving Him. And Jesus loved them, too.

The children were happier than they had ever been because they had seen Jesus, the Son of God.

Jesus loved those little children and is still the Friend of children today. Aren't you glad that Jesus loves the little children?

18

A LITTLE MAN CLIMBS A TREE

(Luke 19:1-10)

ZACCHAEUS was a rich tax collector who lived in a town near Jericho. He collected money from all of the people in his town for the Roman government.

Zacchaeus heard one day that Jesus was going to Jerusalem with His disciples. The Master was going to pass through the village where Zacchaeus lived. Zacchaeus had heard much about Jesus and now he wanted to see Him.

This tax collector was just a little man. He was very small.

As the great crowd came along with Jesus, little Zacchaeus could not see over all the heads. He pushed through the crowd, but still he could not see. There was nothing to stand on.

Suddenly Zacchaeus noticed a tree which was growing along the road. He ran ahead of the crowd and climbed into the tree. Now he could easily see Jesus as He passed by.

Soon the great crowd came moving down the road. When Jesus came near the tree, He looked up and saw the little man.

"Zacchaeus, make haste and come down," said Jesus. "Today I must stay in your house."

Of course Zacchaeus was surprised. How did Jesus know

he was up there in the tree? How did He know his name?

Just think, Jesus was to spend a day in his home! Zacchaeus had expected to get only a glimpse of Jesus. Now Jesus was to visit his house.

It did not take Zacchaeus long to come down from the tree. You can be sure of that. He hurried to Jesus and took Him home with him.

While Jesus was in his home a change came into the heart of this little man. He had not only received Jesus into his home, but Jesus also entered his heart. That was the happiest day of his life. He now had a Friend who would help him to be honest and true.

"Lord, half of what I own I will give to the poor," Zacchaeus told Jesus. "I will return four times as much as I have taken from any man."

When Jesus comes into our hearts we become changed, too. He helps us to become honest and true also.

Does Jesus live in your heart?

19

JESUS IS CRUCIFIED

(Matthew 27:31-54; Mark 15:20-39; Luke 23:26-48;
John 19:16-37)

Not everyone loved Jesus as Zacchaeus did. Cruel people took Jesus to a hillside where He was to be crucified. They forced Him to carry an ugly, heavy, wooden cross on His back. He was sad and, oh, so tired.

The cross was so heavy that Jesus fell as He tried to carry it. A man named Simon stepped forward from the crowd. He carried the cross up the hillside for Jesus.

In the great crowd that followed there were many of Jesus' friends. His disciples were there — Peter, James, John, Andrew, Philip and others. They were all very sad. But they could do nothing to help Jesus.

At last Jesus, the soldiers and all the people reached the place on the top of the hill called Calvary. Simon put the cross on the ground. The soldiers laid Jesus upon it. They nailed His hands and His feet to the wooden cross. A crown of sharp thorns was put on His head.

As the soldiers were doing all this, Jesus looked up into heaven. He prayed, "Father, forgive them, for they do not know what they are doing."

Above His head on the cross the people wrote the words, "Jesus of Nazareth, the King of the Jews." This was written in three different languages.

The soldiers put the cruel cross, with Jesus hanging on it, into the ground. There they left God's Son to die.

There were two other men crucified with Jesus. They were bad men. One hung on each side of Him. One of these robbers turned his head toward Jesus and said, "Lord, remember me when You come into Your Kingdom."

"Today," Jesus replied, "you will be with Me in Paradise." That man was made happy.

Jesus looked lovingly toward Mary, His mother, and said, "Woman, behold your son." He then turned to John, His dear friend, and said, "Behold your mother." From that time John cared for the mother of Jesus as he would his own mother.

While Jesus hung there on the cross the people mocked Him. They told Him to come down from the cross and save Himself. "He saved others," they said, "Himself he cannot save."

Just at noon-time darkness as black as night came down over all the earth. God took away the light of the sun. The darkness remained for three long hours.

At the end of the third hour Jesus cried to His Father, "My God, My God, why have You forsaken Me?"

A short time later Jesus spoke again. He said, "I thirst." Someone took a sponge, filled it with vinegar, put it on a reed and gave it to Him to drink.

Jesus then said in a loud voice. "It is finished." His work was done. He had paid for our sins.

A moment later He cried out loudly, "Father, into Thy hands I commend My spirit." He bowed His head and gave up His life.

The suffering was over. Jesus had given His life for sinners. He died that those who love Him might live.

When Jesus died, God shook all the earth by an earthquake. The people were afraid. They said to each other, "What kind of man was this Jesus?"

The Roman captain who stood near the cross said to his soldiers, "Truly, this man was the Son of God."

As Jesus died, a strange thing happened in the Temple. The curtain in front of the holy place, where only the high priest could enter, was torn from the top to the bottom. No longer do we have to go before a high priest to God. Jesus has become our High Priest. Now we can pray to God through Jesus Christ.

Three days later Jesus rose again from the grave.

PAUL AND SILAS IN THE JAIL

(Acts 16:16-40)

AT one time Paul and his friend Silas were in Philippi. They had been preaching in that city and telling the people about Jesus.

At first there was no church in that city. Someone said to Paul, "People go to the river, to pray there."

So Paul and Silas went to the river. There they found some women. Paul and Silas sat down and talked with the women. They told them about Jesus.

The women were glad to hear the wonderful story of Jesus. They had never heard it. Many of them learned to love Jesus.

After a while there was a big church in Philippi. Many people believed on Jesus.

One day Paul and Silas were taken by an angry crowd of people and dragged before the rulers of the city. They said, "These men are Jews and are making trouble in our city. They teach the people to do what is against the law of the Romans."

The cruel rulers pulled the clothes from Paul and Silas. They ordered that the two men be beaten with heavy sticks.

After many hard, cruel blows, these faithful followers of the Lord Jesus were thrown into a prison. A jailor was told to watch them carefully. He took the bruised and bleeding men to a dungeon. He fastened their feet and hands between boards so that they could not even move. There they sat, in the dark jail.

That night, about midnight, Paul and Silas were praying and singing praises to God. Suddenly the earth began to shake. The whole prison was shaken. Every door was opened. The chains fell off the hands and feet of the prisoners. But none of them tried to escape.

The jailor was awakened suddenly by the terrible earthquake. He saw all of the doors open. He was sure his prisoners had escaped. He thought, *If all the prisoners are gone, I will be killed.*

He took out his sword to kill himself.

Just then he heard Paul call to him. "Do yourself no harm," said Paul. "We are still here."

Then the jailor hurried to Paul and Silas. He saw that all of the prisoners were still there. He fell on his knees. "Sirs, what must I do to be saved?" he asked.

Paul answered, "Believe on the Lord Jesus Christ and you will be saved." Then he told the jailor all about the Savior.

The jailor and his family did believe on Jesus. They showed by their lives that they loved Him.

Do you love and serve Jesus, too?